STAR WARS®

CONSTABLE
ZUVIO

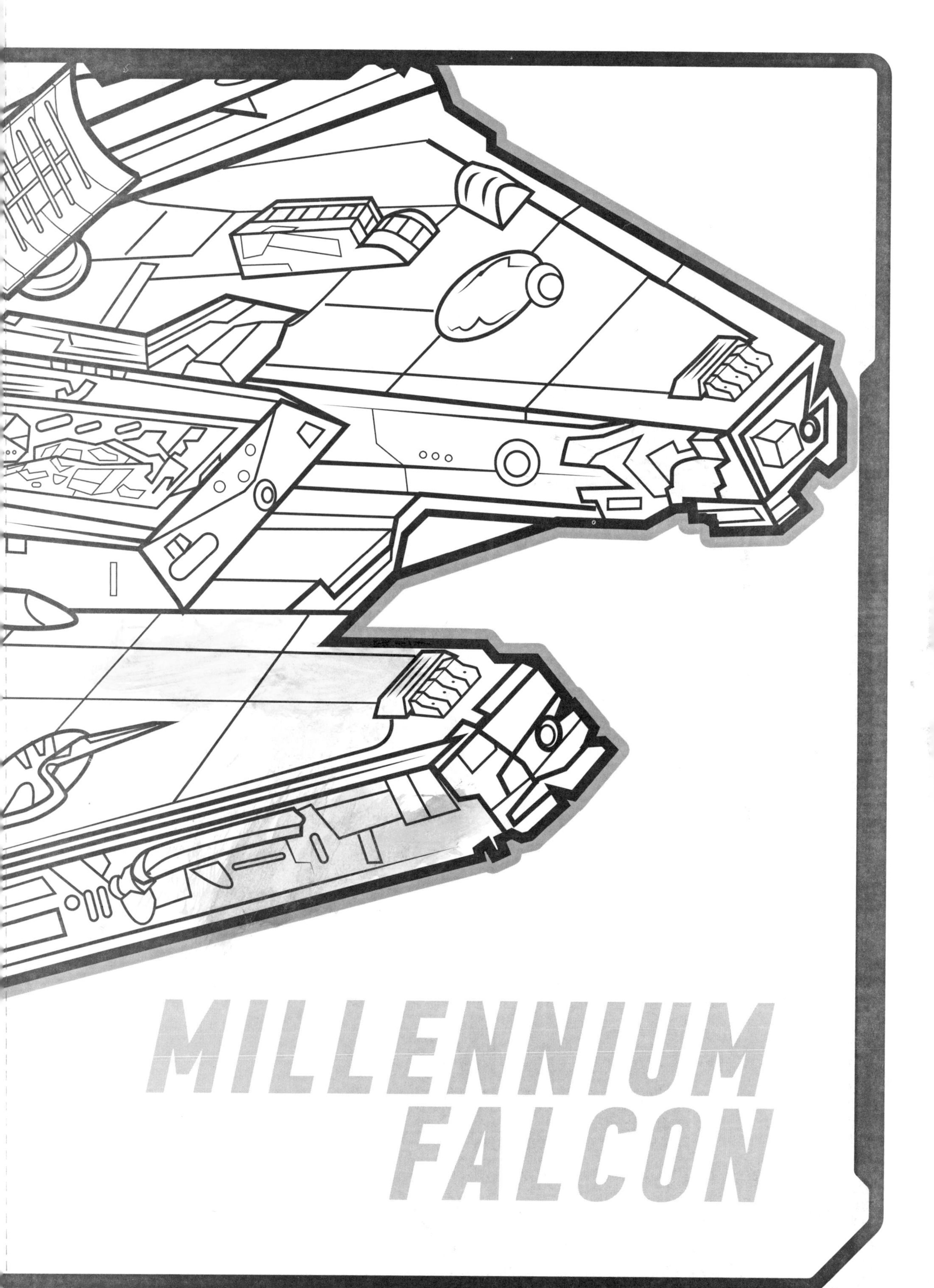
MILLENNIUM
FALCON

FIRST ORDER STAR DESTROYER

SARCO

RB-8
ASTROMECH
DROID

FINN

STAR WARS

RESISTANCE WORD SEARCH

X	A	J	Q	K	G	R	N	P	H	O	I	D
S	W	M	I	L	L	E	N	N	I	U	M	F
A	T	I	P	Q	U	Y	I	U	O	C	H	A
S	B	A	N	G	F	K	F	V	T	H	A	L
T	C	5	R	G	M	N	E	O	N	E	N	C
R	D	R	V	F	Q	O	I	J	N	W	S	O
O	U	L	S	R	I	P	N	O	Z	B	O	N
M	V	W	V	2	U	G	R	Y	7	A	L	A
E	D	M	T	D	E	E	H	B	A	C	O	Z
C	R	K	L	2	M	E	F	T	D	C	L	Y
H	O	L	C	A	C	3	P	O	E	A	E	W
S	I	R	D	R	K	M	S	T	I	R	I	J
E	D	E	S	P	E	E	D	E	R	2	A	B
C	O	G	E	C	N	A	T	S	I	S	E	R
P	F	H	R	E	P	O	O	R	T	B	B	8

RESISTANCE
TROOPER
REY, FINN
SPEEDER
LUKE, LEIA
HAN SOLO

BB-8
C-3PO
R2-D2
MILLENNIUM
FALCON
CHEWBACCA

X-WING
STARFIGHTER
POE DAMERON
ASTROMECH
DROID

STAR WARS

FIND THE DIFFERENCE

Circle the drawing of Rey that is different.

REY

REY'S SPEEDER

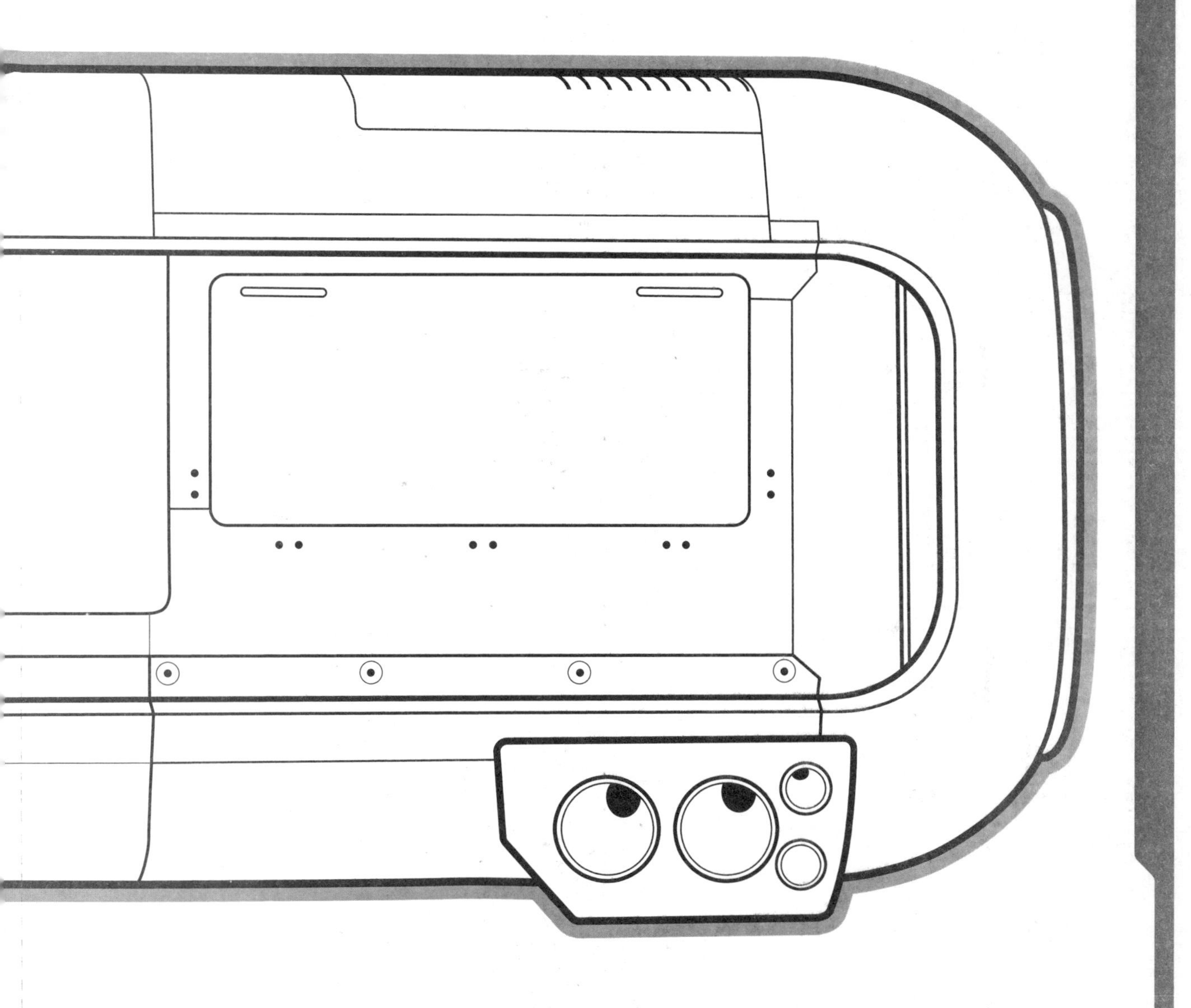

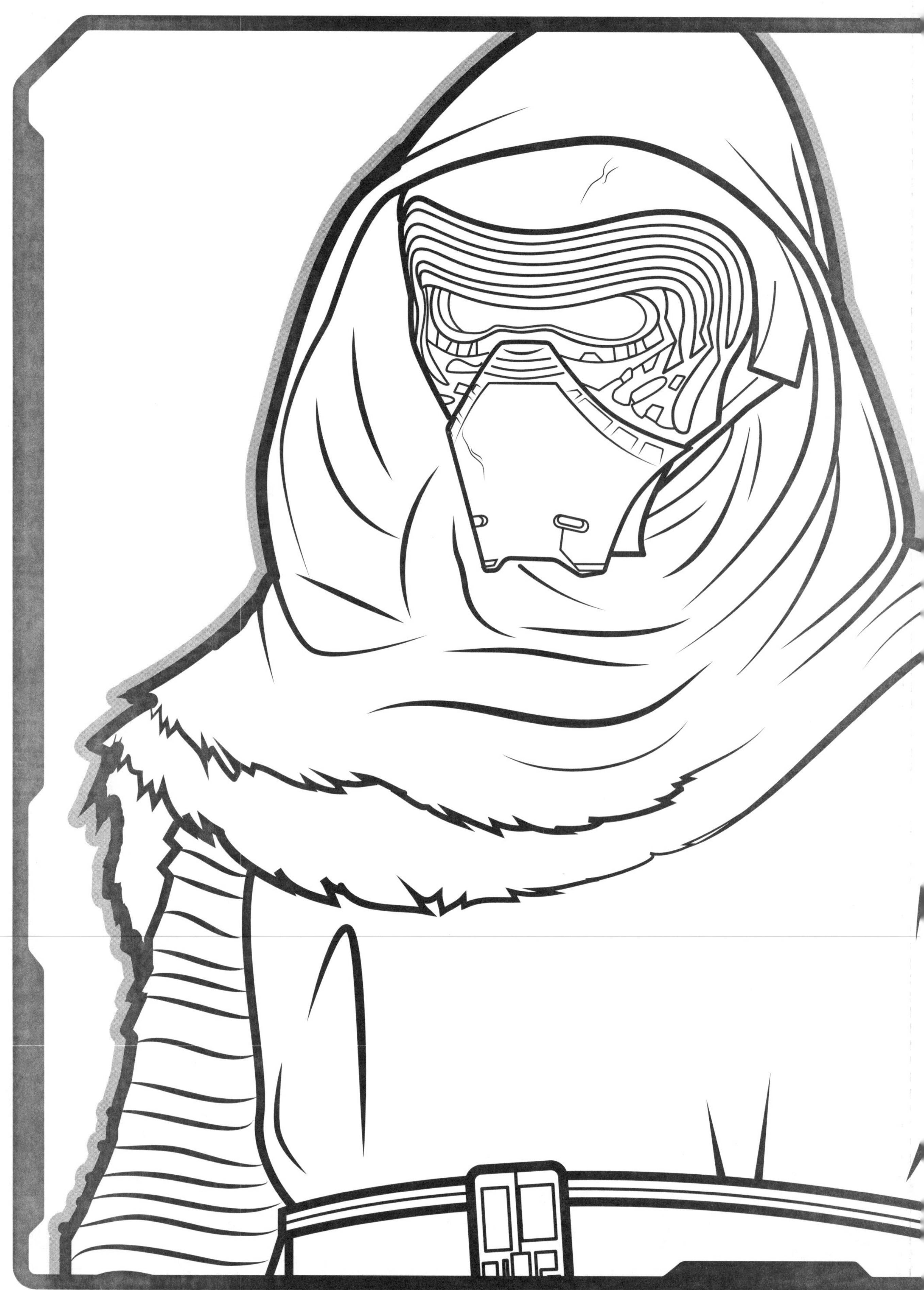

KYLO REN

CAPTAIN
PHASMA

STAR WARS

FIND THE DIFFERENCE

Circle the drawing of Kylo Ren that is different.

ANSWER: D

STAR WARS

Make different words from the letters in

CAPTAIN PHASMA

POSSIBLE ANSWERS: SAP, PAN, CAN, TAN, STAIN, PAIN, RAT, MAT, MIT

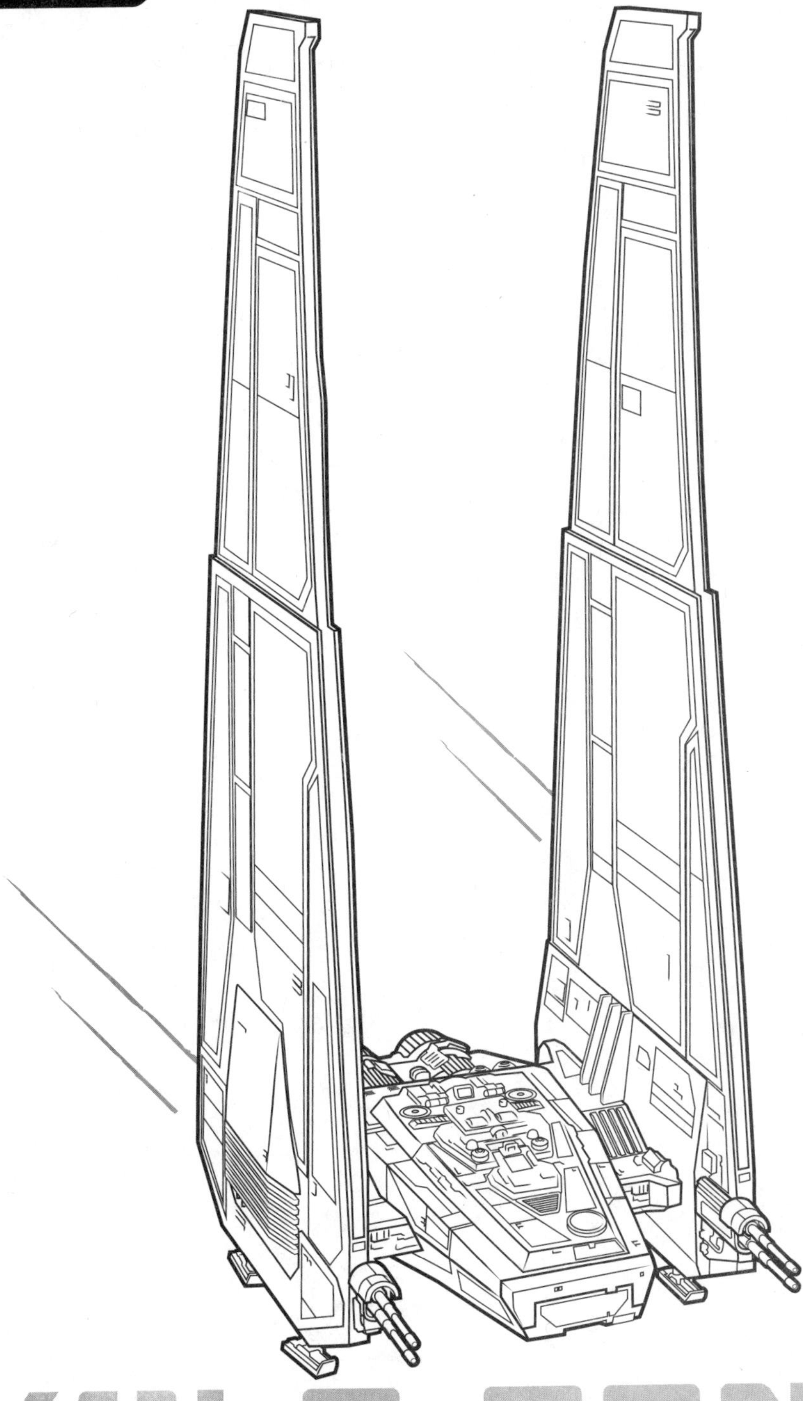

KYLO REN'S COMMAND SHUTTLE

GUAVIAN
DEATH
GANG

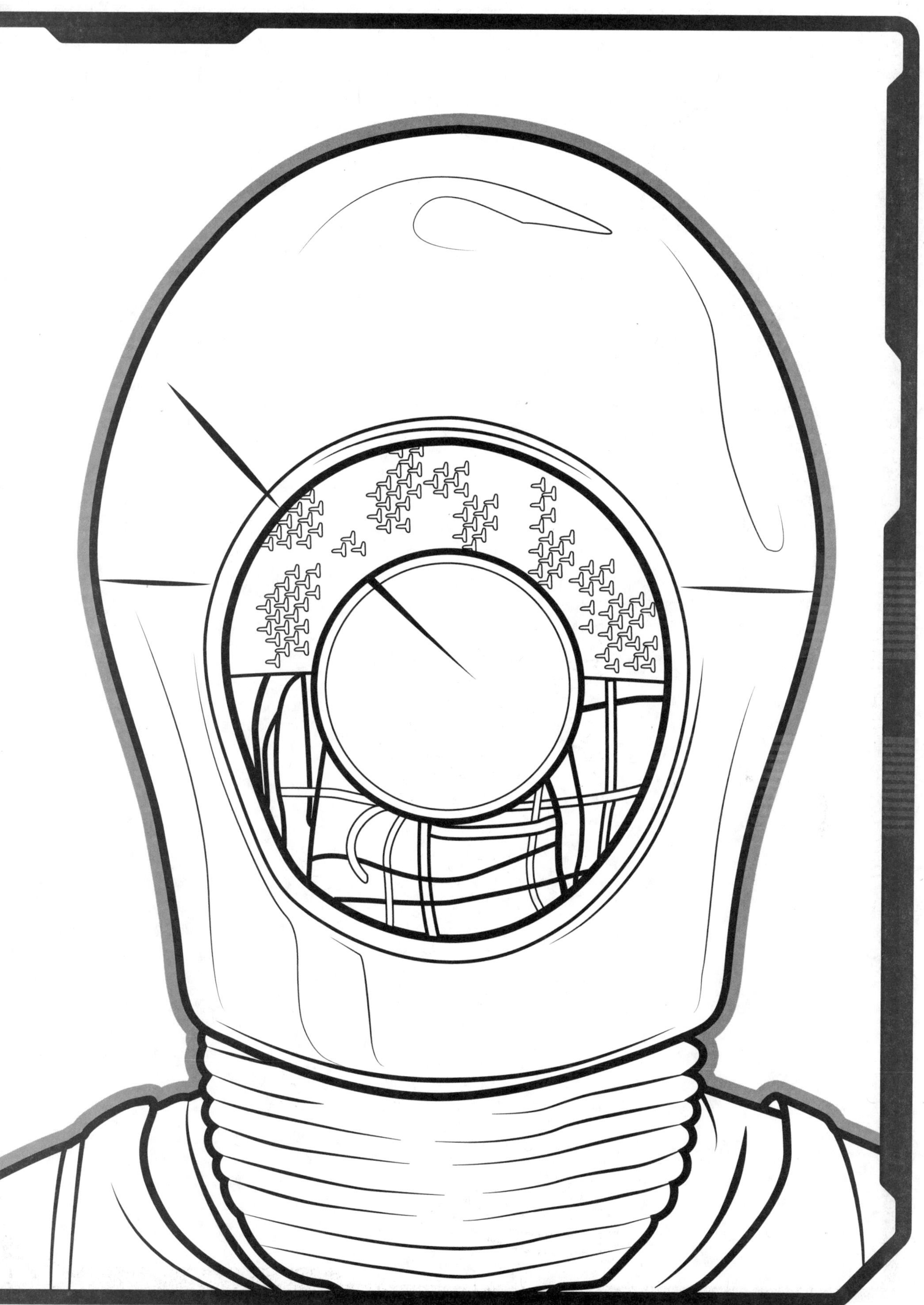

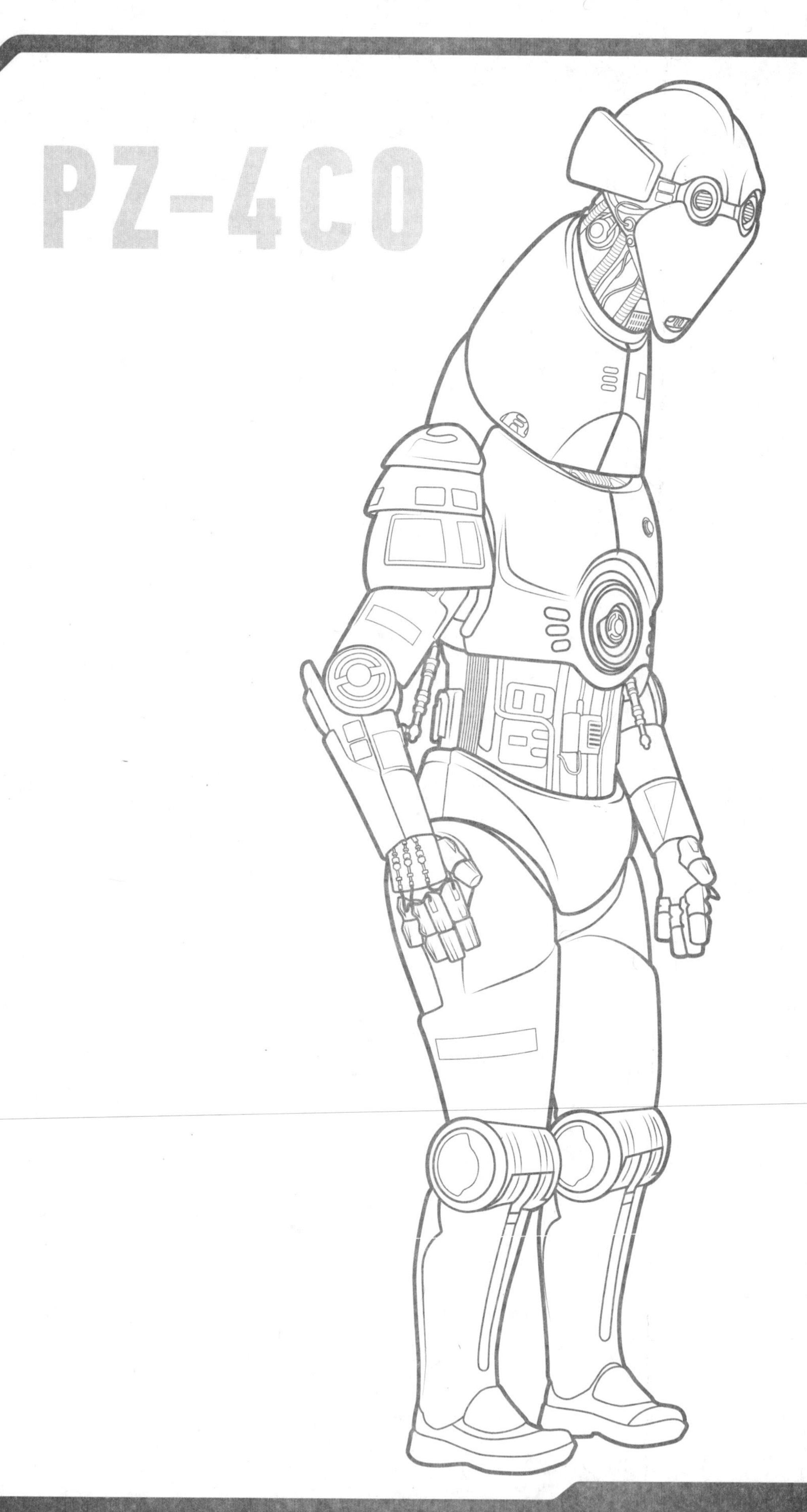
PZ-4CO

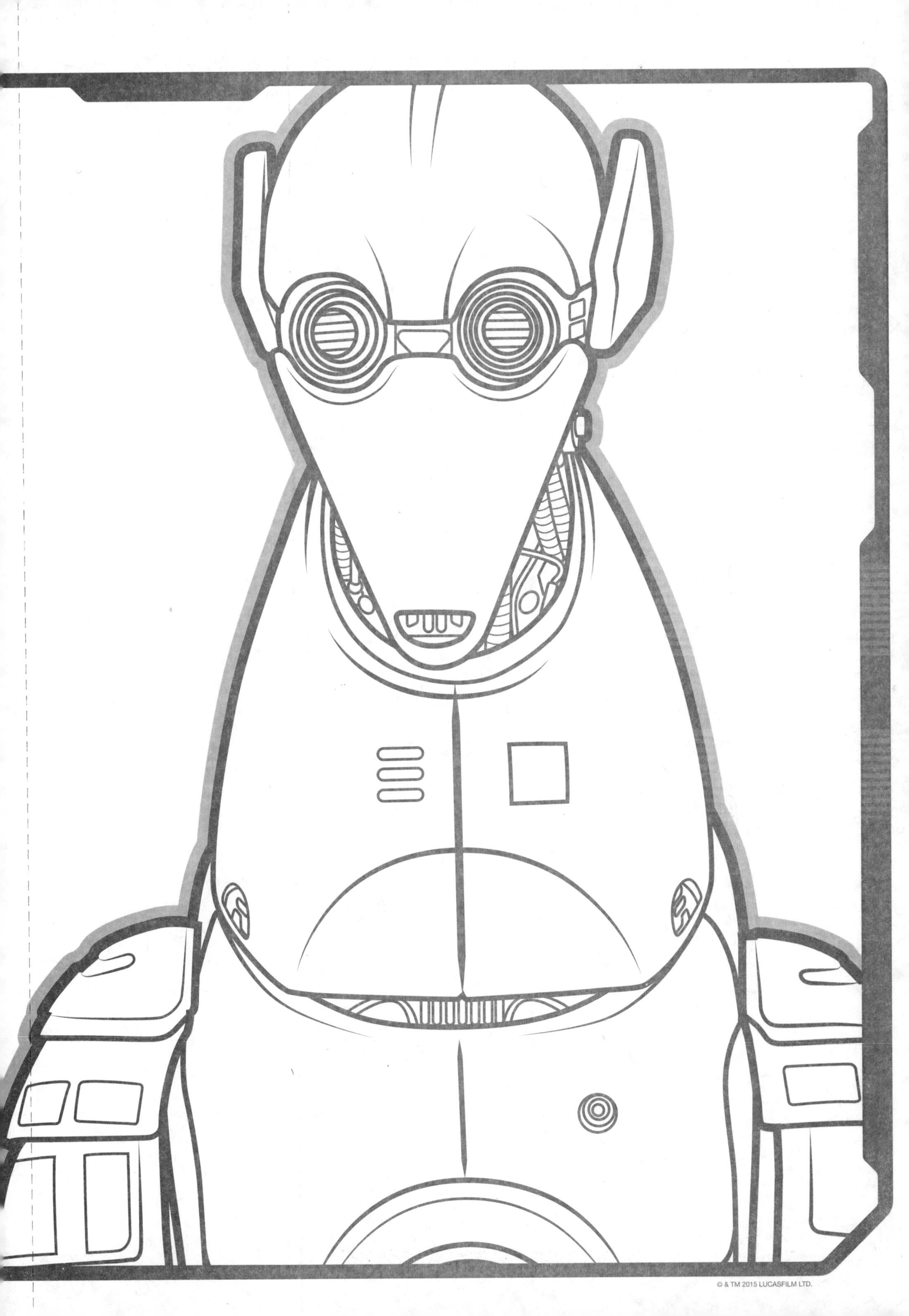

RESISTANCE TROOPER

TEEDO

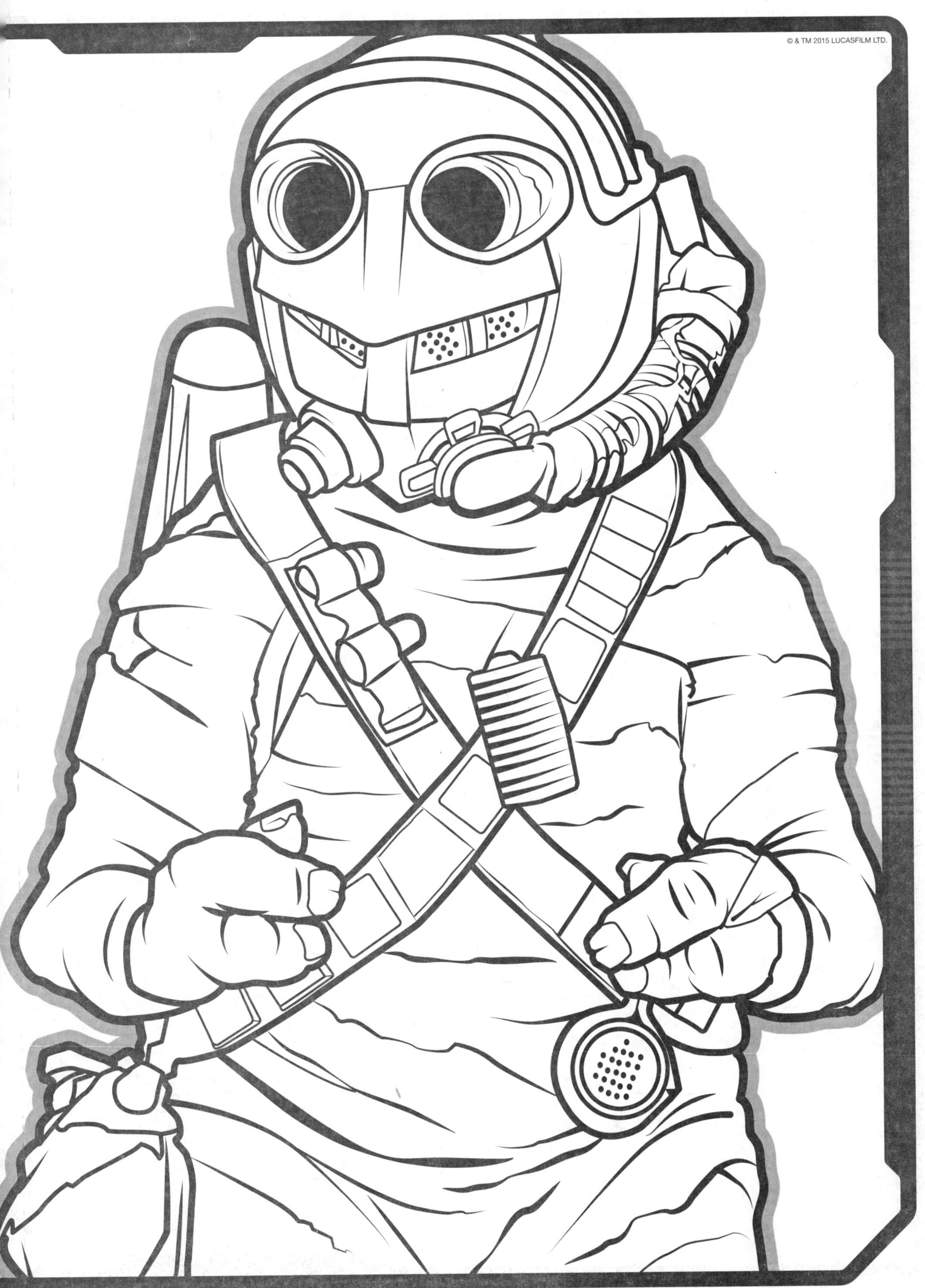

CHEWBACCA

R2-D2

C-3PO

POE
DAMERON

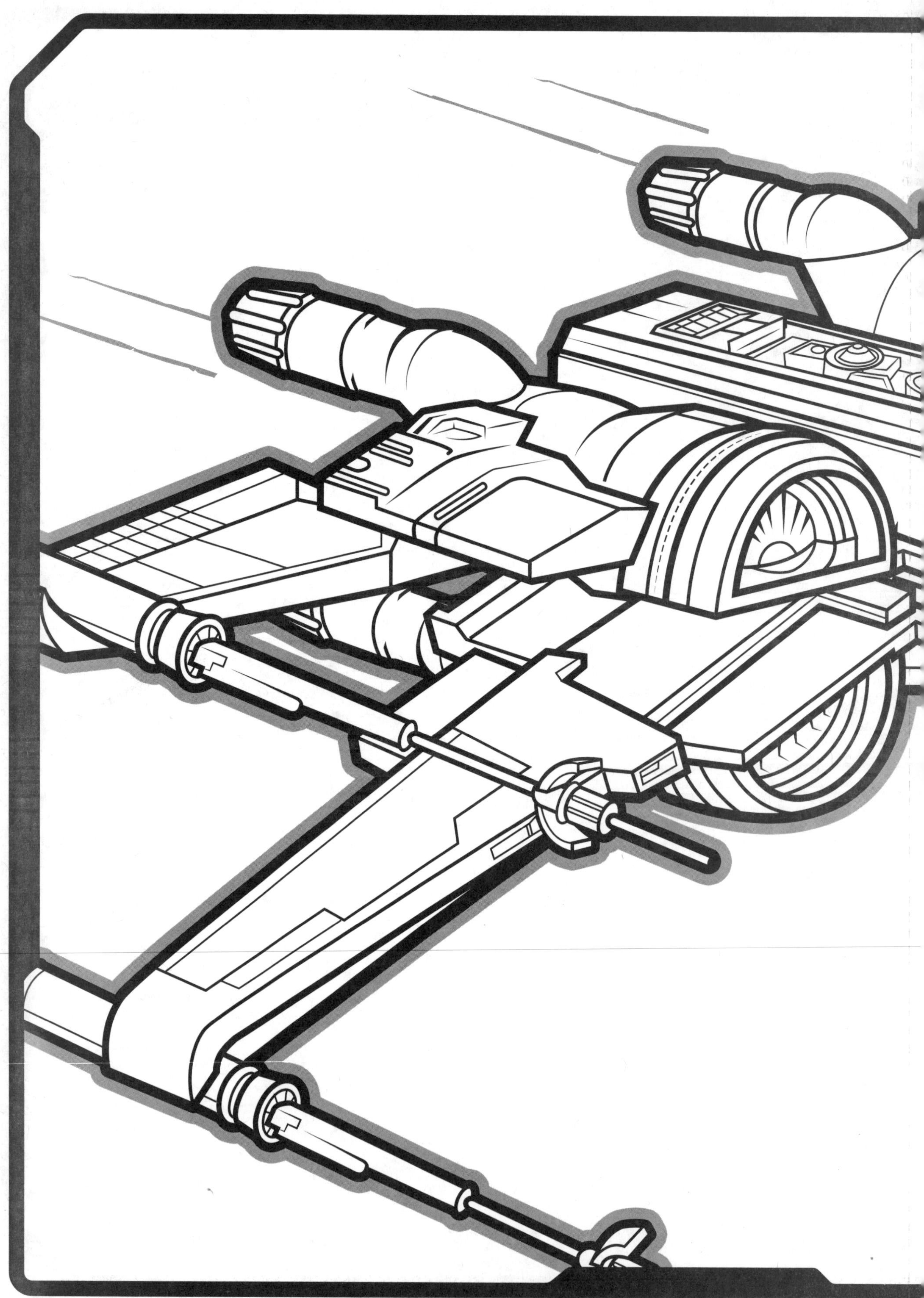

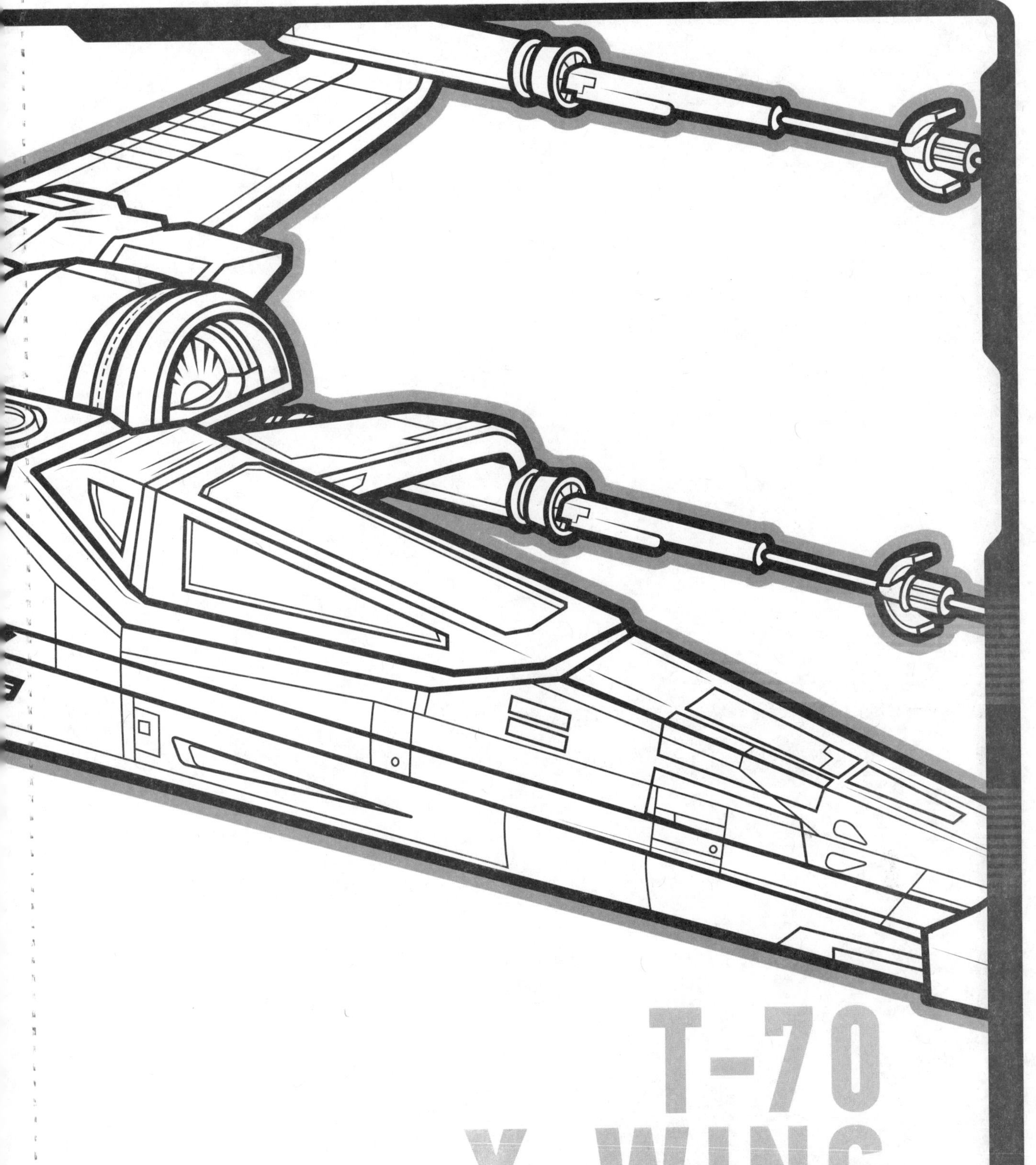

T-70 X-WING STARFIGHTER

STAR WARS
X-WING STARFIGHTER MAZE
Lead Poe through the maze to his fighter!
START
FINISH

STAR WARS

WHICH PATH TO FOLLOW?

Which path leads Finn and BB-8 to Rey and her speeder?

ANSWER: B

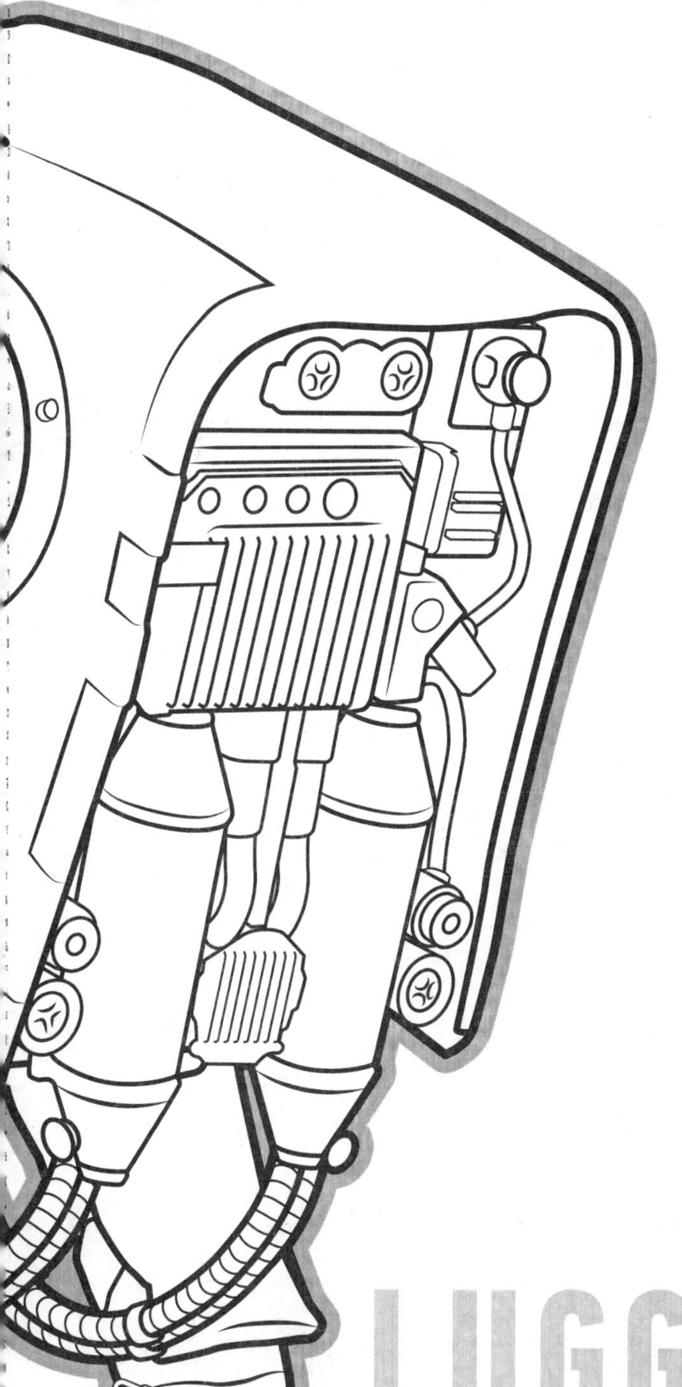

LUGGABEAST

TIE
FIGHTER
PILOT

FIRST ORDER TIE FIGHTERS

STAR WARS

FIRST ORDER TROOPERS

Draw lines to match each name to the correct trooper.

1. STORMTROOPER

2. FLAMETROOPER

3. SNOWTROOPER

4. TIE FIGHTER PILOT

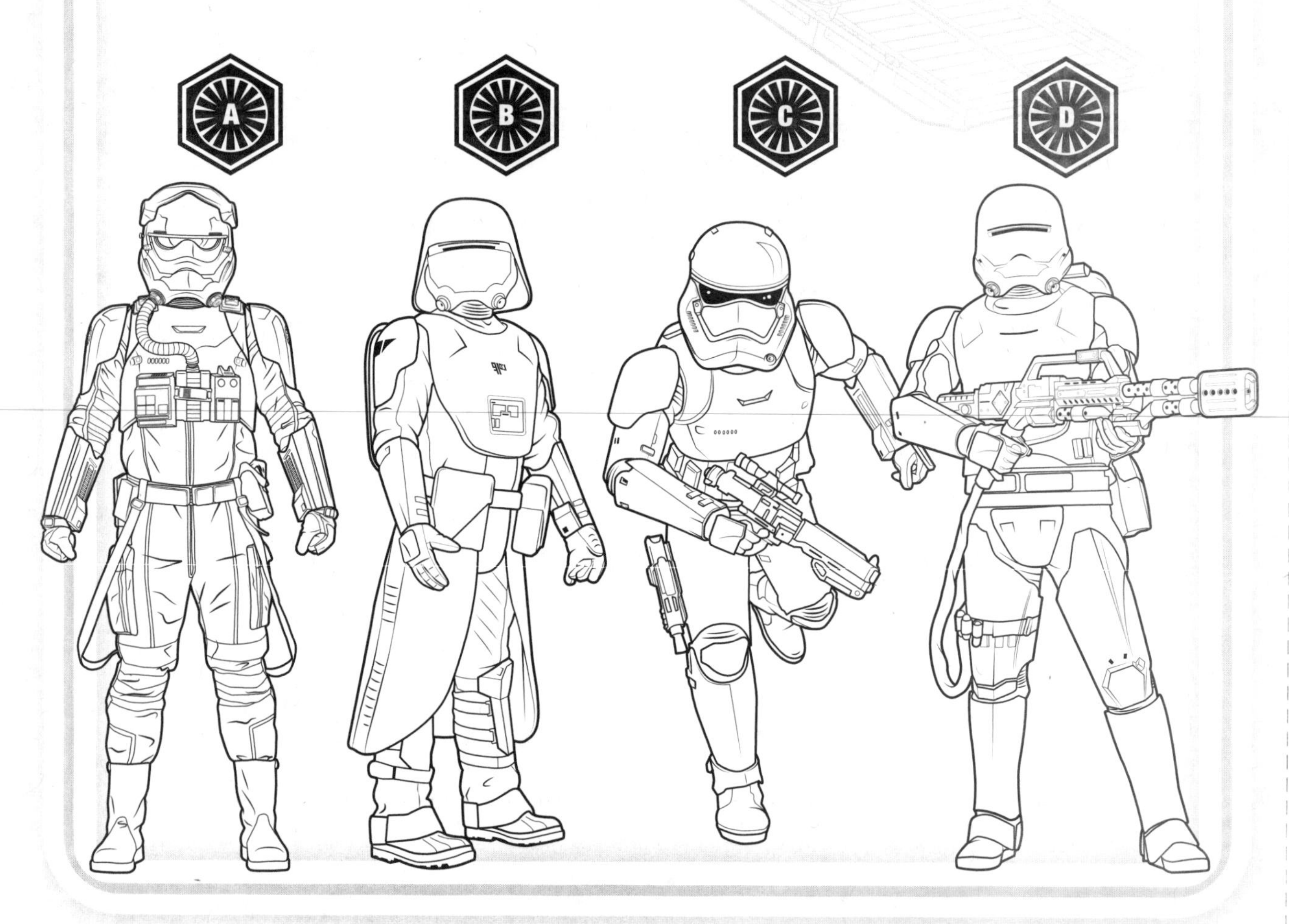

ANSWERS: 1–C, 2–D, 3–B, 4–A

STAR WARS

TIE FIGHTER MAZE

Lead the TIE fighter pilot through the maze to his fighter!

START

FINISH

STAR WARS

SHOW OF FORCE!

How many stormtroopers do you count?

ANSWER: 21

STAR WARS

FIRST ORDER WORD SEARCH

C	D	S	B	L	A	S	T	E	R	F	C	F
S	A	E	T	R	I	F	L	E	N	I	D	L
T	U	P	S	A	B	P	O	W	E	R	I	A
O	T	P	T	T	R	A	L	M	O	S	J	M
R	I	A	R	A	R	P	W	Y	Z	T	K	E
M	E	Q	D	E	I	O	B	R	Q	O	S	T
T	F	R	A	K	M	N	Y	C	T	R	P	R
R	I	S	R	Y	F	E	P	E	U	D	O	O
O	G	D	K	L	T	O	L	H	R	E	N	O
O	H	E	S	O	U	G	R	E	A	R	M	P
P	T	F	I	R	A	V	Y	C	A	S	L	E
E	E	H	D	E	W	Z	J	K	E	D	M	R
R	R	G	E	N	H	I	S	N	O	K	E	A
E	F	S	N	O	W	T	R	O	O	P	E	R
R	E	Y	O	R	T	S	E	D	R	A	T	S

STORMTROOPER
SNOWTROOPER
FLAMETROOPER
TIE FIGHTER
STAR DESTROYER

FIRST ORDER
SUPREME LEADER
CAPTAIN PHASMA
KYLO REN
POWER

DARK SIDE
FORCE
BLASTER
RIFLE

FIRST ORDER SNOWTROOPER

© & TM 2015 LUCASFILM LTD.

FLAMETROOPER

FIRST
ORDER RIOT
CONTROL
TROOPER